To Doug
Happy travelling!
2015

GJ For Keston, Barnaby, Toby and Theo

For Julie, Wyatt, Flynt and Bronwyn

First published in 2013 Grobags Children's books

With thanks to: Elizabeth Jones (my fantastic Mum), Alex Duncan, Limpet Marketing (big thanks to Steve and Joe), Carol Downing, Lillian Sears, Anne Blee, Rachel Morrison, Sharon Kennett, Steve Fowler and Phil Lloyd.

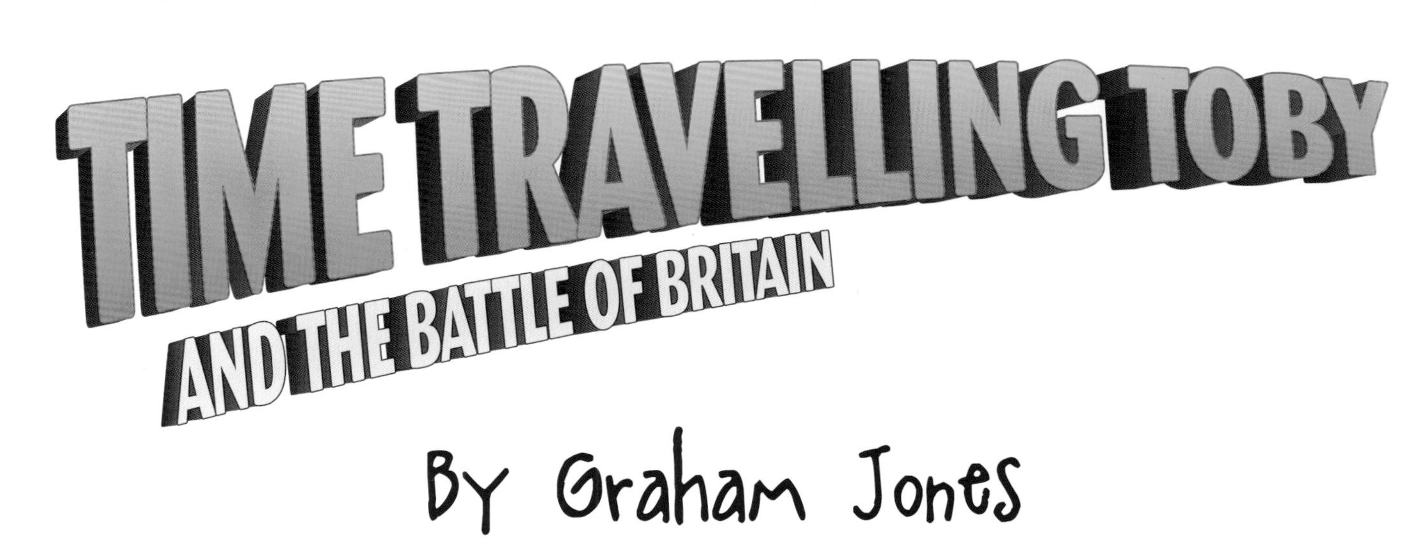

By Graham Jones

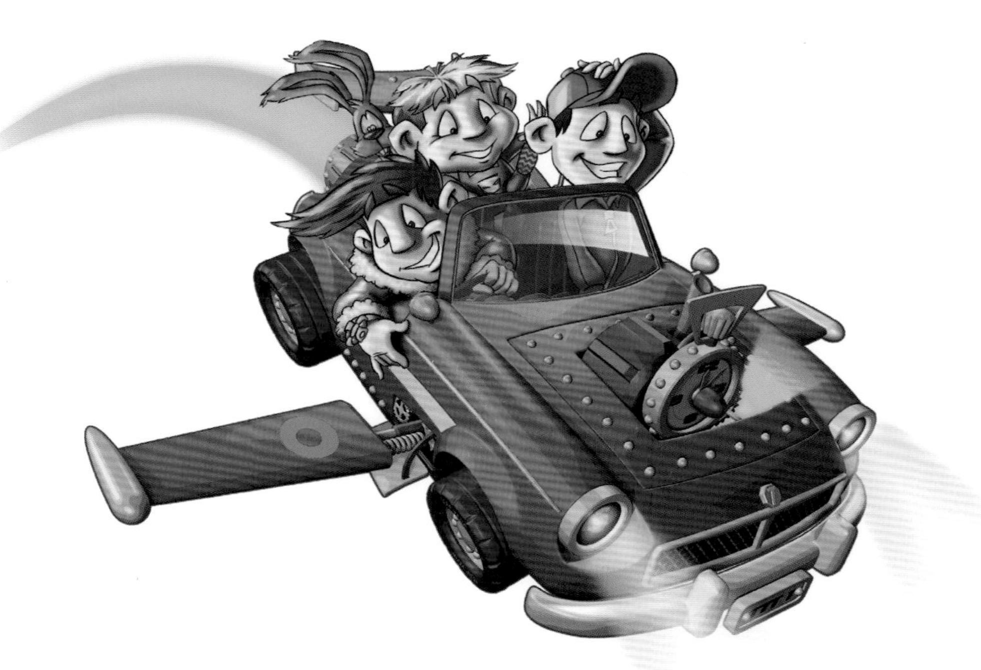

Illustrated by Neil Parkinson

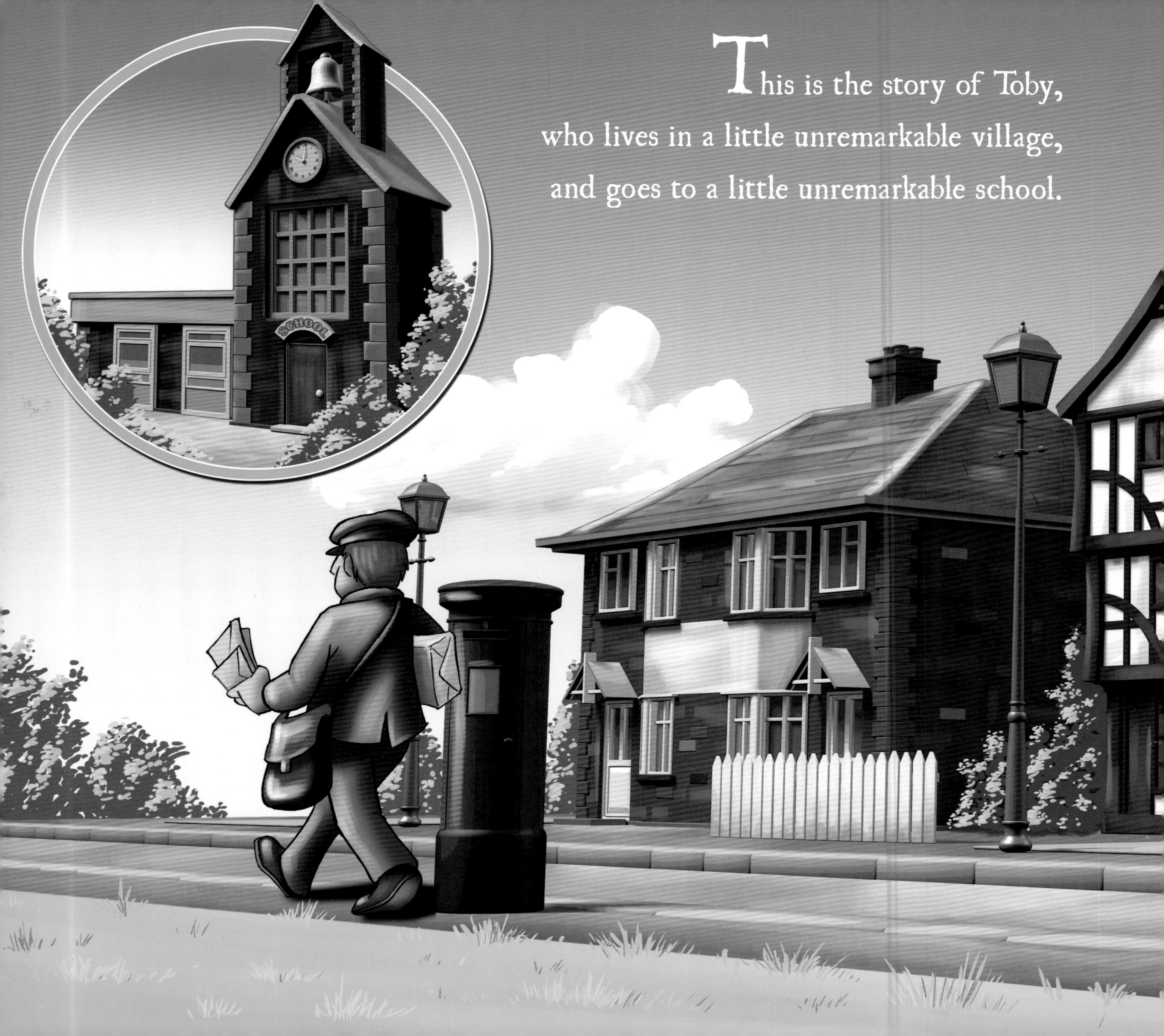

This is the story of Toby,
who lives in a little unremarkable village,
and goes to a little unremarkable school.

But Toby has a humongous secret,
which is SoooOOOO
incredibly cool!

By the way Toby has two brothers, one big and one little;
a Mum and Dad, two Nans, and a Nanma. Two dogs, three fish and two rabbits –

And his secret is...

...a time machine that looks just like a sports car!

KEEP OUT!
LEAP YEAR
LEAP YEAR

Toby's time machine is orange,
and has loads of really neat gear,
four comfy seats, a 3-spoke wheel, a go faster stripe,
and a dial to choose what to visit and the exact time and year!

Toby's secret is shared by his brothers,
but nobody else has a clue.
Today they've planned an adventure
to give them something exciting to do.

Into the car they all clamber,
and Toby, who's last, shuts the door.
"Lets visit the Battle of Britain" says Toby,
as he puts his foot to the floor!

The car begins to [illegible] as the dial spins round and round.
Toby's little brother says, "are we there yet?" as the car slowly lifts off the ground.

A BANG! and a FLASH! of bright light surrounds them,
in a jiffy the journey is over,
with a crash and a bump the car comes to rest...

...on the edge of the White Cliffs of Dover!

"Watch Out!" a voice calls from behind,
"We're under attack from enemy fire."
the boys look up and see to their horror,
a Stuka bomber climbing higher and higher.

The nose of the plane dips down slowly,
engines roaring with a whistling sound.
It gets louder, and louder, and louder, and louder,
until a bomb hurtles by to the ground.

"Crikey!" a man says, "You were lucky!
I'm amazed that you came to no harm.
Quick, start your car or whatever it is,
we need to raise the alarm."

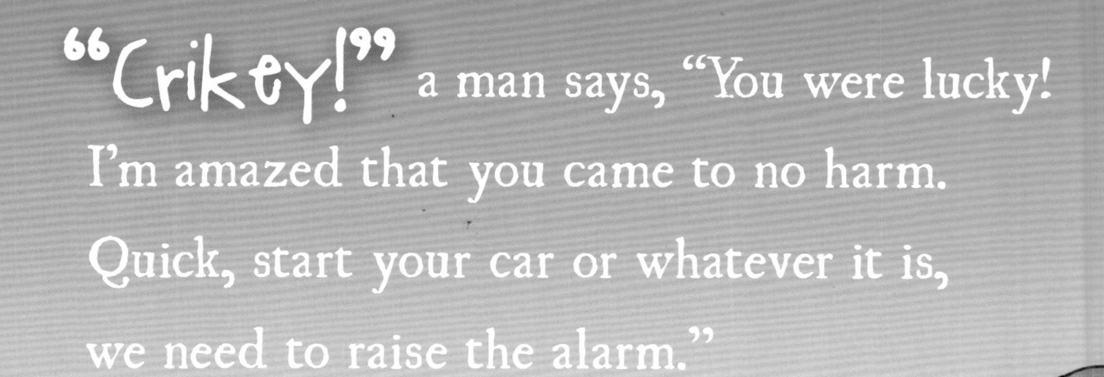

They jump in and turn the ignition,
German bombers are filling the sky.
They know they have to move quickly
but nobody knows how to fly!

No matter! The car's taking over,
as the bombers head out of sight.
It knows what to do without any help
Toby's time machine's joining the fight!

The car has no guns for attacking,
it won't let the boys come to harm.
By flying inland to fighter command,
it can help them raise the alarm!

"Scramble Scramble Scramble" yells Toby

"Get those spitfires up in the air!
Pilots and planes, all get ready.
Give the enemy one heck of a scare!"

All over the sky, planes are fighting, as the boys watch, safe under cover.
"Come on," Toby shouts, "watch your backside, shoot them down one after another!"
RAT-ATA-TAT!!

The Spitfires soon scent a victory
as the Luftwaffe starts to retreat.

The warning has made all the difference
and the skirmish is almost complete!

The boys jump and shout with excitement,
knowing they've helped win the battle.
But all of a sudden there's a FLASH! and a BANG!
as the car starts to shake and to rattle.

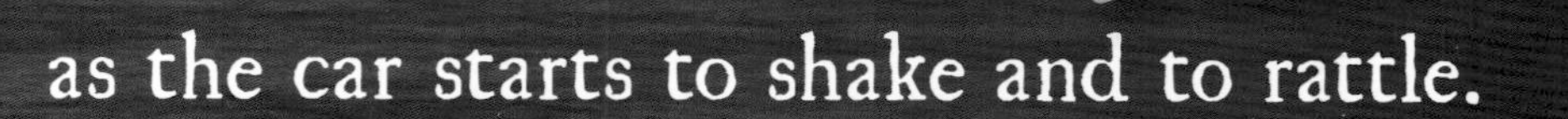

The dial starts to spin as the boys buckle up,
Toby's adventure is almost complete.
In the blink of an eye the car comes to rest
at the end of their unremarkable street!

"Come on," Toby says, "we're home just in time for a drink and a victory supper."

They sit down with their Dad and eat bangers and mash, washed down with a great British cuppa!

So that's how we won the Battle of Britain.
Something Toby will never forget.

Next time if you're good we'll tell you the tale of how he and Lord Nelson first met!

LEAP YEAR
LEAP YEAR

KEEP OUT!

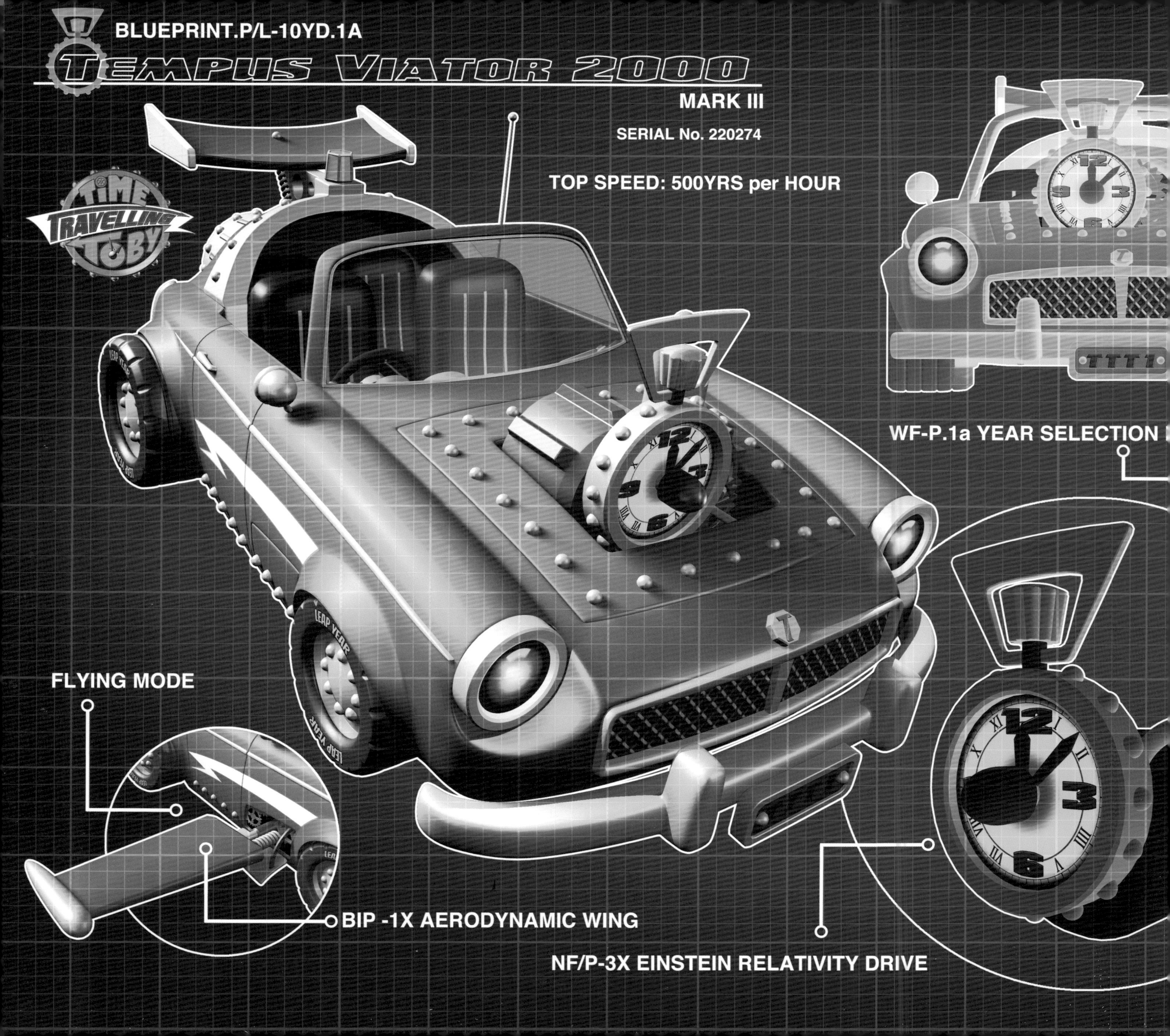
BLUEPRINT.P/L-10YD.1A
TEMPUS VIATOR 2000
MARK III
SERIAL No. 220274
TOP SPEED: 500YRS per HOUR
TIME TRAVELLING TOBY
WF-P.1a YEAR SELECTION
FLYING MODE
BIP -1X AERODYNAMIC WING
NF/P-3X EINSTEIN RELATIVITY DRIVE
LEAP YEAR
TTT1

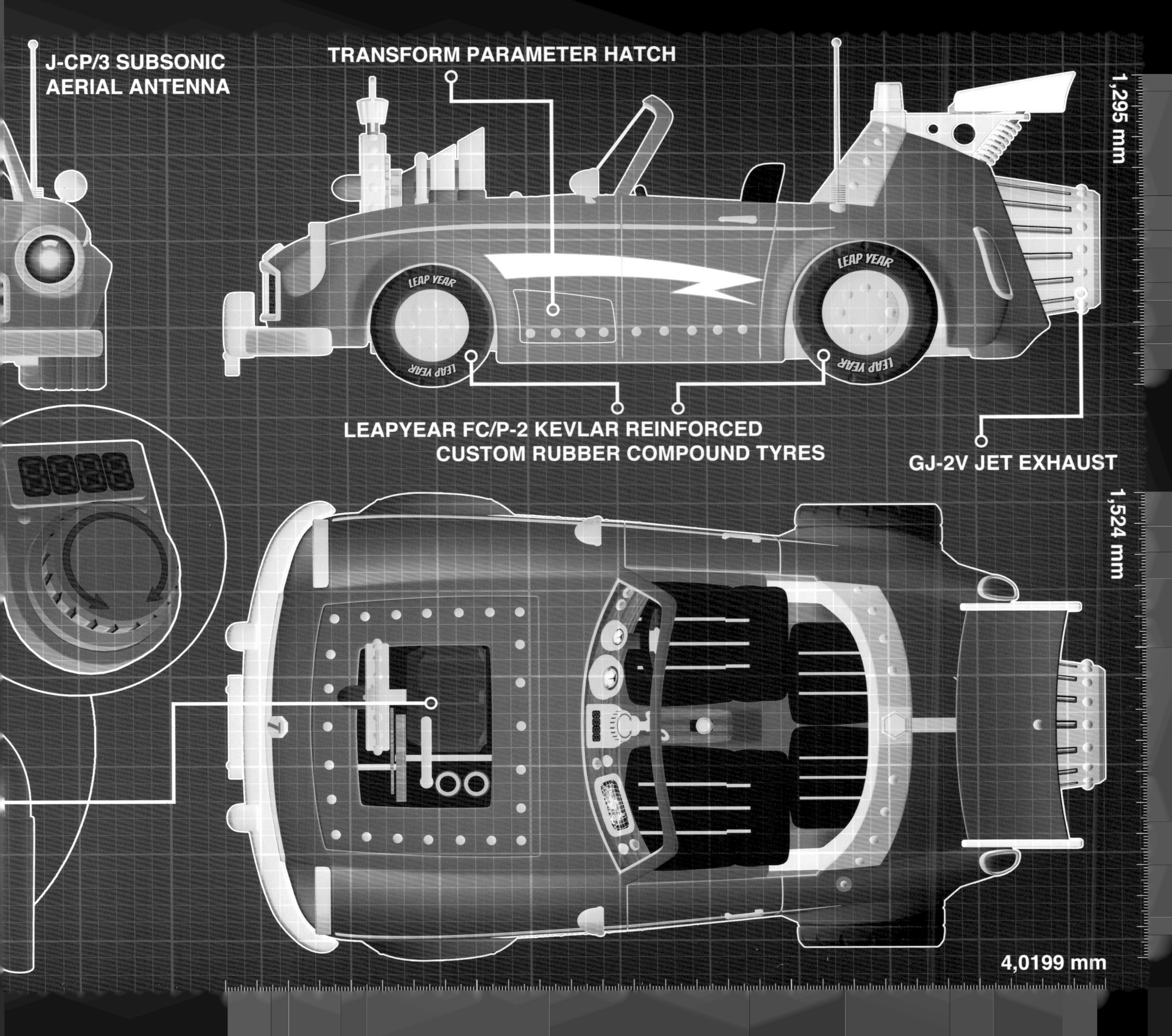
J-CP/3 SUBSONIC
AERIAL ANTENNA
TRANSFORM PARAMETER HATCH
1,295 mm
LEAP YEAR
LEAP YEAR
LEAP YEAR
LEAP YEAR
LEAPYEAR FC/P-2 KEVLAR REINFORCED
CUSTOM RUBBER COMPOUND TYRES
GJ-2V JET EXHAUST
1,524 mm
4,0199 mm

Facts about the Battle of Britain

The Luftwaffe was the name for the German airforce during World War II. During the Battle of Britain, the Luftwaffe caused severe damage to the Royal Air Force and major British cities. However, it did not achieve the air superiority that was required to prepare for a planned German invasion.

The Junkers Ju 87 or Stuka is a German dive bomber from the Second World War. The Stuka was easily recognisable by its gull wings and its "Jericho Trumpet" wailing siren. Although very effective, the Stuka was vulnerable to attack by Spitfires and Hurricanes during the Battle of Britain.

The Messerschmitt Bf 109, often called Me 109, was the main German World War II fighter. The Me 109 was widely used in the battle of Britain and was the most produced fighter plane in history, with a total of 33,984 units made from 1936 up to April 1945.

The Battle of Britain is the name given to the Second World War air campaign waged by the German Air Force (Luftwaffe) against the United Kingdom during the summer and autumn of 1940. The name derives from a famous speech delivered by Prime Minister Winston Churchill in the House of Commons: "...the Battle of France is over. I expect that the Battle of Britain is about to begin."

The White Cliffs of Dover are cliffs which are part of the English coastline facing France. The cliffs are over 100 metres high and are composed partly of white chalk. The cliffs have great symbolic value because they face towards Continental Europe across the narrowest part of the English Channel, where invasions have historically threatened.

RAF Fighter Command was formed in 1936 to control the deployment of fighter planes. It served throughout the Second World War and earned great fame during the Battle of Britain, when it was said "the Few" held off the Luftwaffe attack on Britain and ultimately helped win the war.

The Supermarine Spitfire is a British single-seat fighter plane that was used by the Royal Air Force throughout the Second World War. The Spitfire was designed by R. J. Mitchell, and incorporated a powerful Rolls Royce Merlin engine. During the Battle of Britain, the Spitfire was widely used, although the more numerous Hawker Hurricane is acknowledged to have been the more influential plane.

The Hawker Hurricane is a British single-seat fighter plane that was designed and built by Hawker Aircraft Ltd. Although largely overshadowed by the Supermarine Spitfire, the aircraft became renowned during the Battle of Britain, accounting for 60% of the RAF's air victories in the battle. More than 14,000 Hurricanes were built during the Second World War.

If you have enjoyed travelling with Toby,
why not join him on his next exciting adventure?

www.timetravellingtoby.com